60 Of The Most Beautiful Classical Piano Solos

PROJECT MUSIC LOVERS

PROJECT MUSIC LOVERS *on* **YouTube**

ISBN: 9781953149039

Copyright © 2020 by Project Music Lovers

Second Paperback Edition: June 2020
First Paperback Edition: March 2020

Contents

Minuet in G major, BWV Anh. 114

from "Notebook for Anna Magdalena Bach"

Christian Petzold
(1677-1733)

1

Arietta (Op. 12, No. 1)

Edvard Grieg
(1843 – 1907)

Poco Andante e Sostenuto

with Pedal

Norwegian Melody (Op. 12, No. 6)

Edvard Grieg
(1843 – 1907)

4

Gymnopédie No. 1

From *Trois Gymnopédies*

Erik Satie
(1866 – 1925)

Nocturne in E-flat Major (Op. 9, No. 2)

Frédéric Chopin
(1810 – 1849)

Polonaise in G Minor (B. 1)

Frédéric Chopin
(1810 – 1849)

Allegro, ma non troppo

Piano

Polonaise da capo al Fine

Prélude in E Minor (Op. 28, No. 4)

Frédéric Chopin
(1810 – 1849)

Prelude in D-flat Major (Op. 28, No. 15)

Frédéric Chopin
(1810 – 1849)

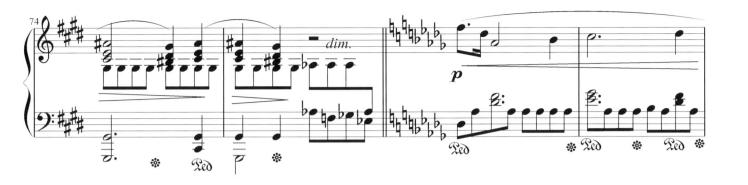

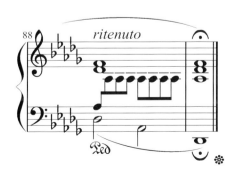

Prelude in B Minor (Op. 28, No. 6)

Frédéric Chopin
(1810 – 1849)

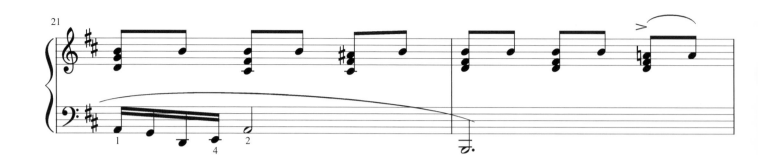

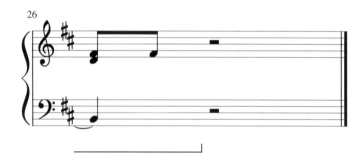

Songs Without Words (Op. 19, No. 6)

Gondola Song

Felix Mendelssohn Bartholdy
(1809 – 1847)

Songs Without Words (Op. 30, No. 3)

Consolation

Felix Mendelssohn Bartholdy
(1809 – 1847)

Songs Without Words (Op. 30, No. 6)

"Venetianisches Gondellied"

Felix Mendelssohn Bartholdy
(1809 – 1847)

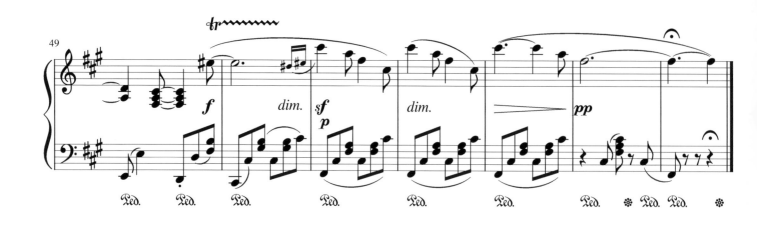

Minuet in F Major No. 11 (HWV 437)

"Little Serenade"

Franz Joseph Haydn
(1732 – 1809)

La Campanella

Franz Liszt
(1811 – 1886)

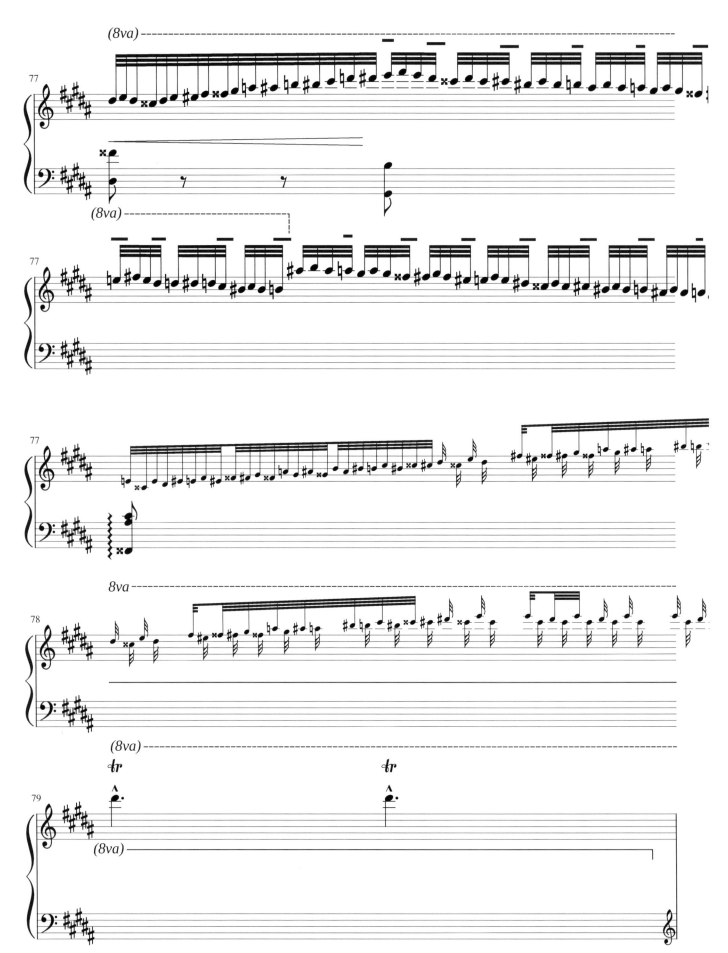

37

38

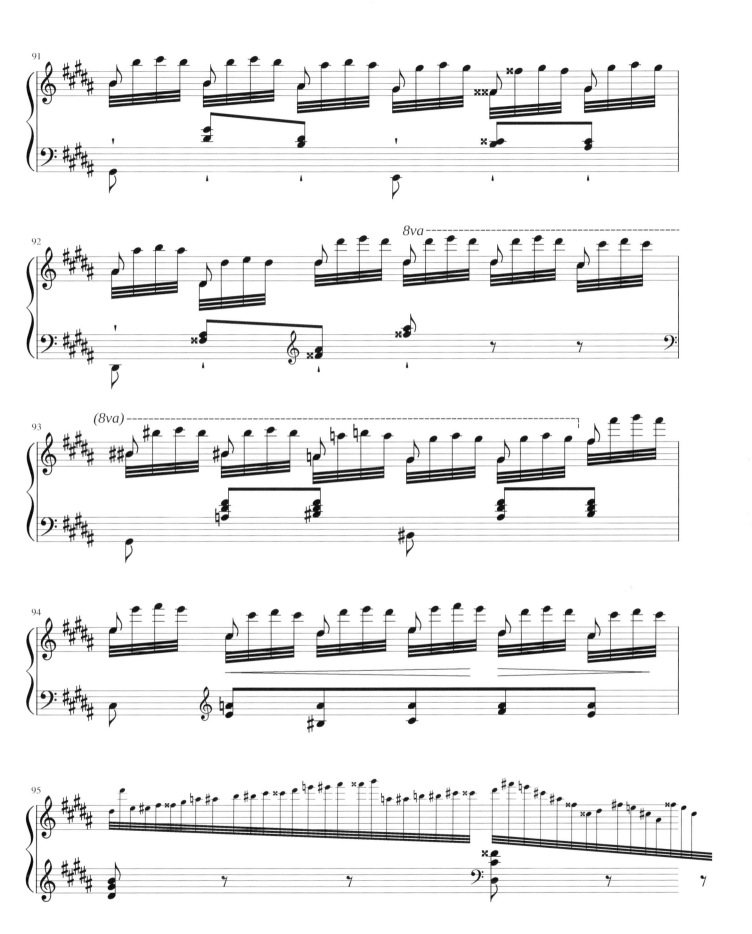

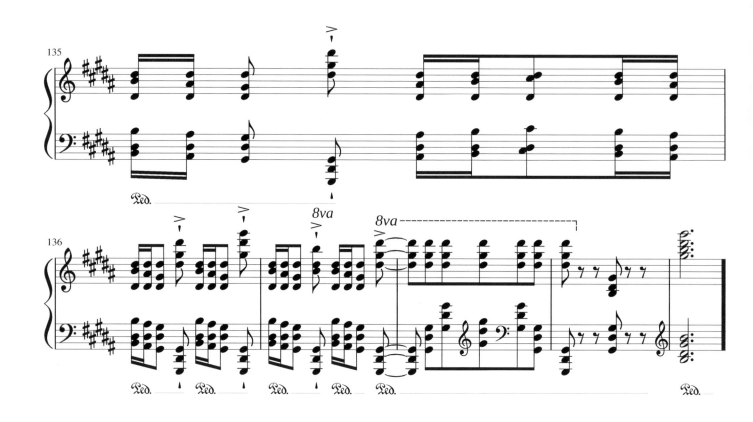

Consolation No. 3 in D Flat Major, S 172

Franz Liszt
(1811 – 1886)

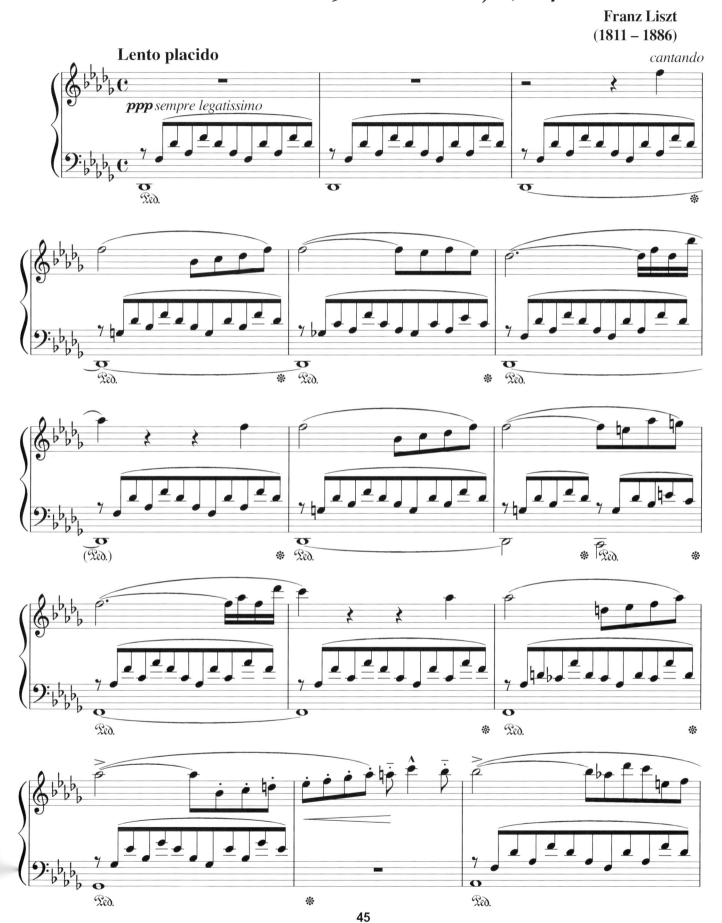

47

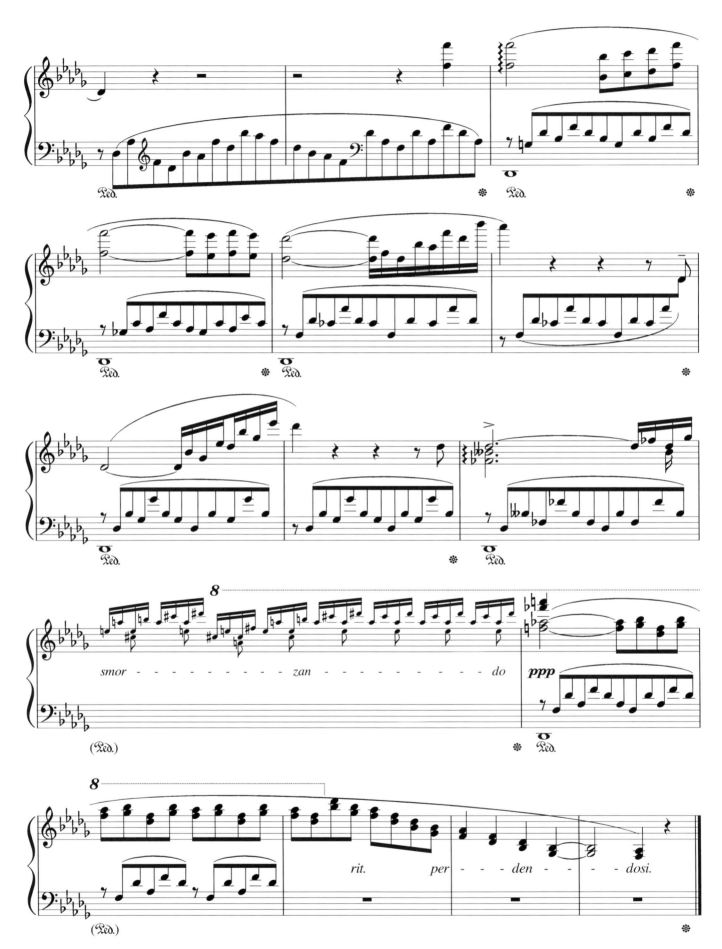

Hungarian Rhapsody No. 6

Franz Liszt
(1811 – 1886)

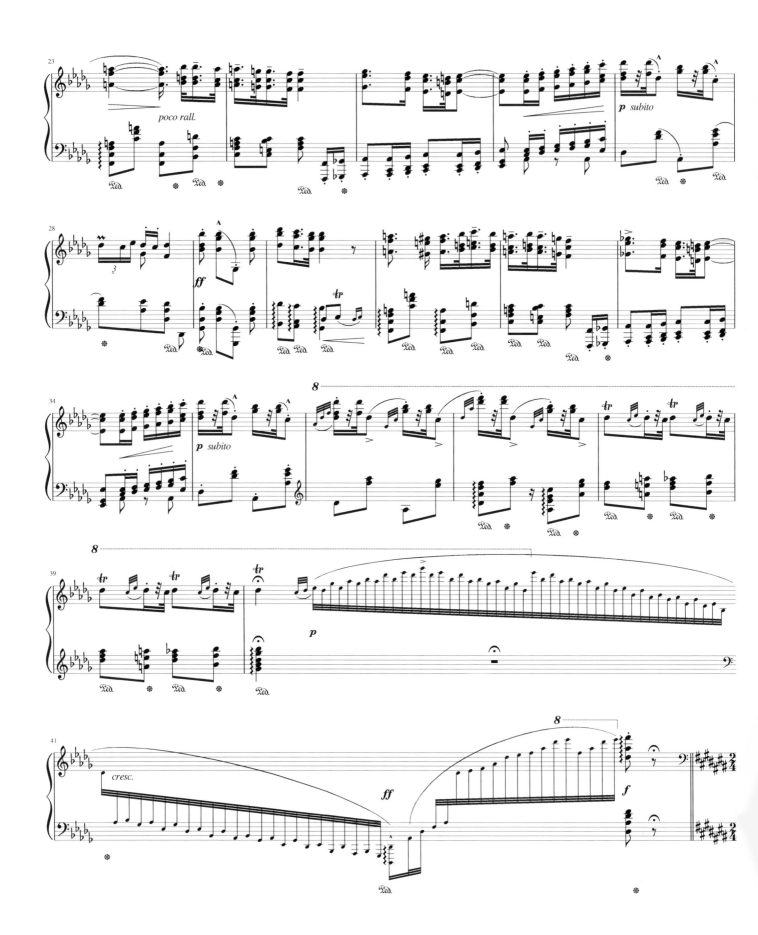

55

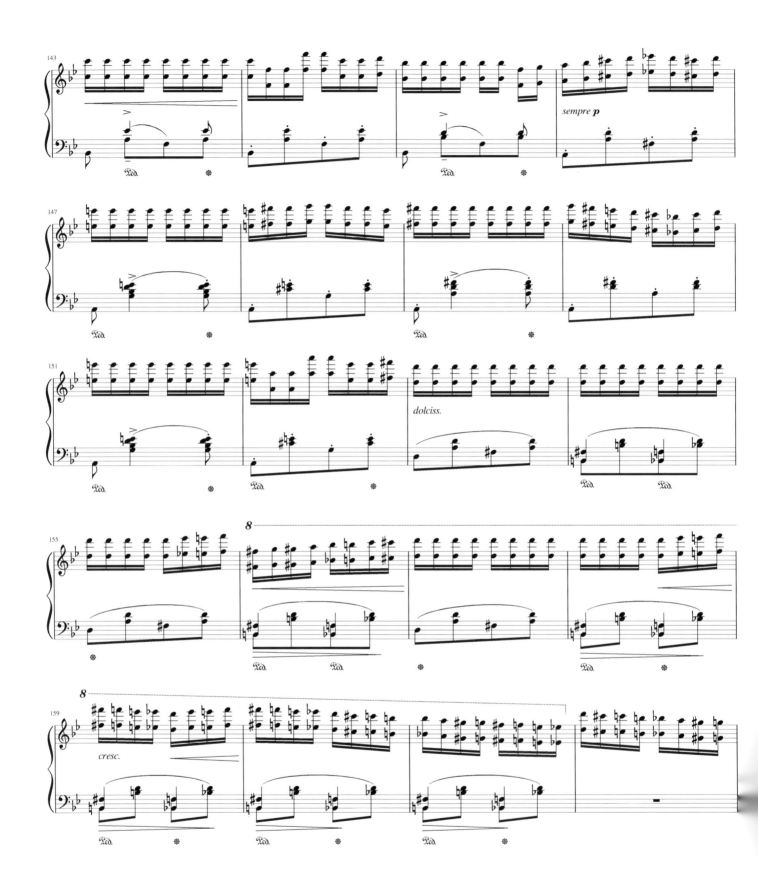

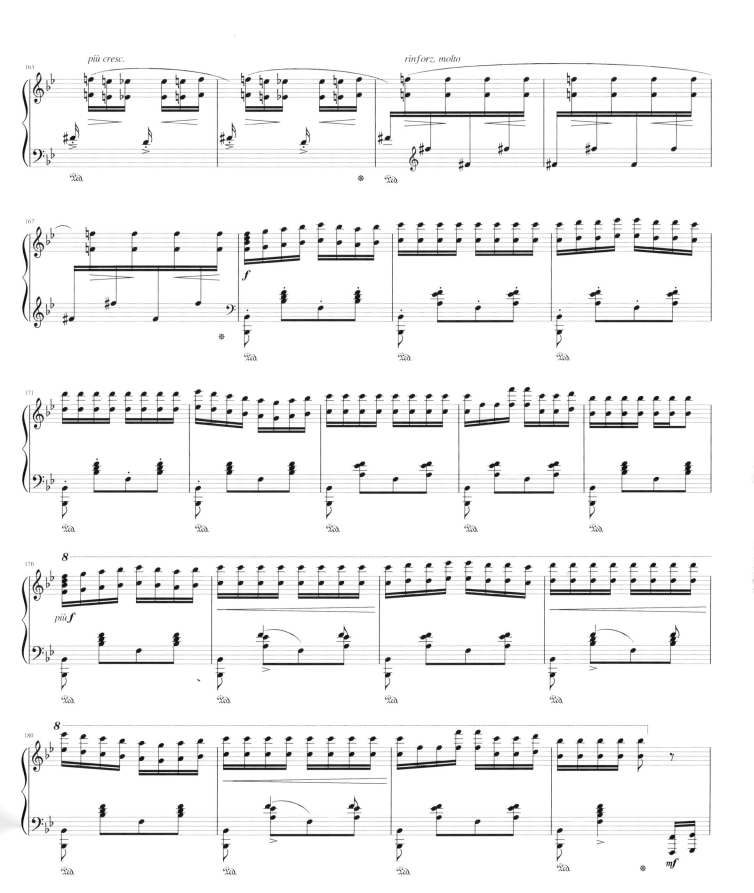

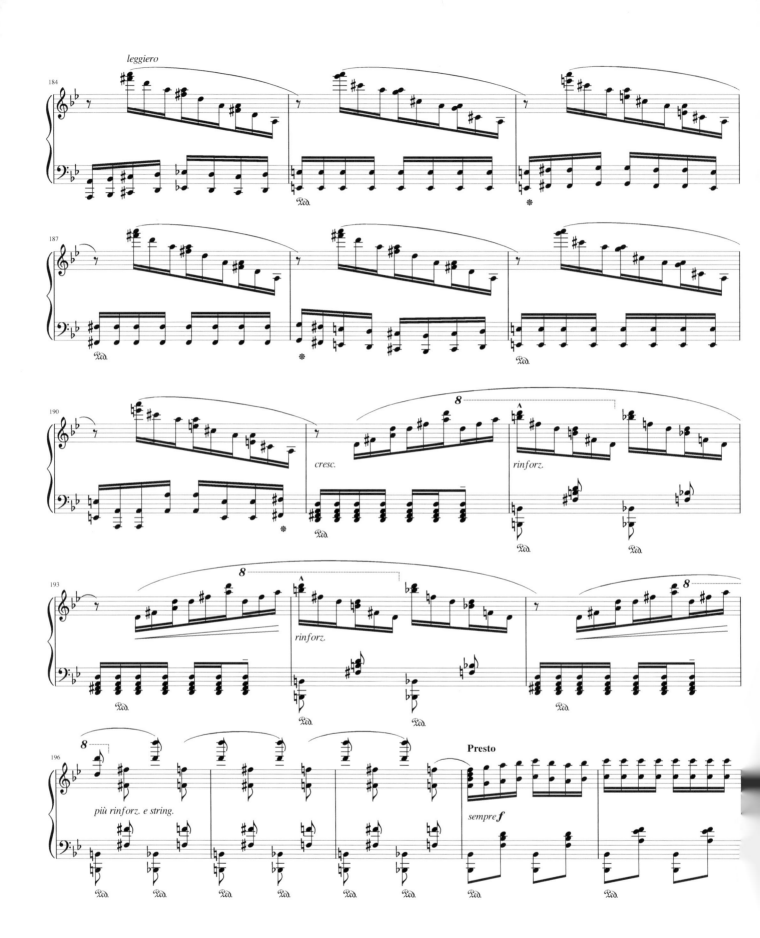

59

Variations on an Austrian Folk Song (Op. 42, No. 1)

Friedrich Kuhlau
(1786 – 1832)

Clair de Lune, 3ʳᵈ Movement

from "Suite Bergamasque" L. 75

Claude Debussy
(1862 – 1918)

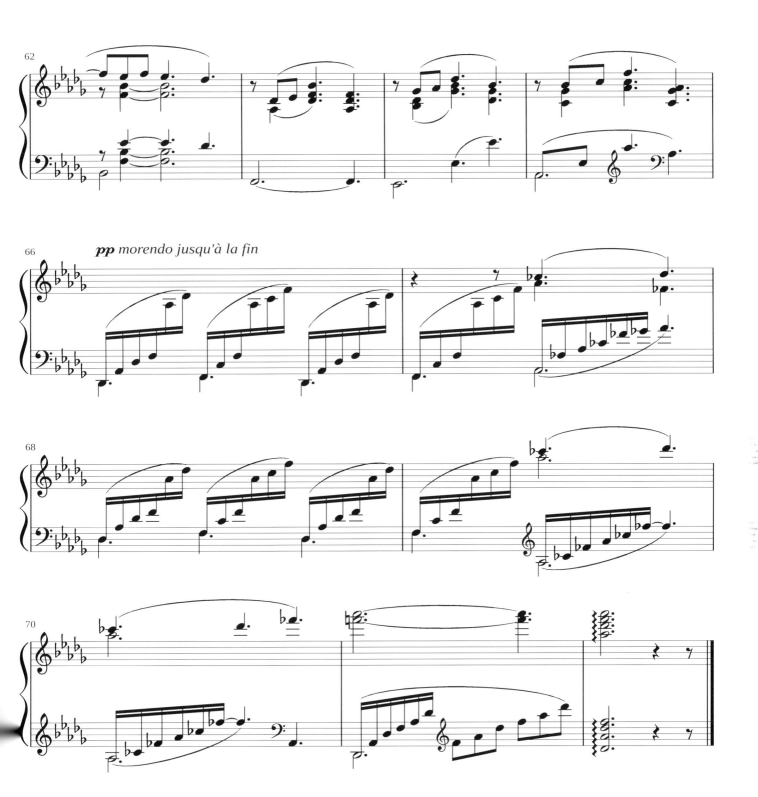

pp morendo jusqu'à la fin

Le Petit Nègre (Op. 28, No. 6)

Claude Debussy
(1862 – 1918)

Gigue in G Major

Georg Philipp Telemann
(1681 – 1767)

Chaconne from Suite in D Minor (HWV 437)

George Frideric Handel
(1685 – 1759)

Variation I

Variation II

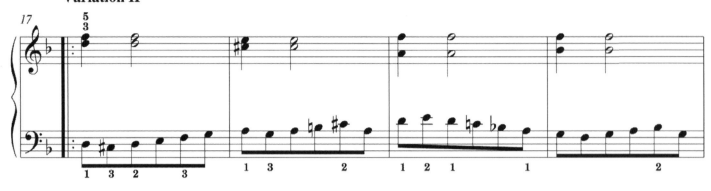

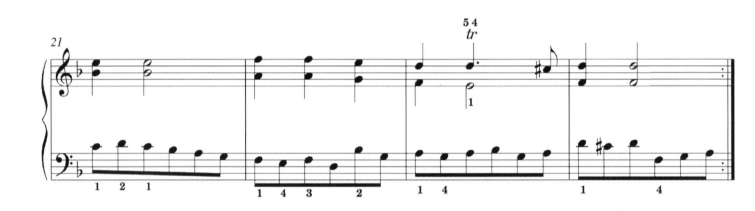

Variation III

Variation IV

Variation V

Variation VI

Variation VII

Variation VIII

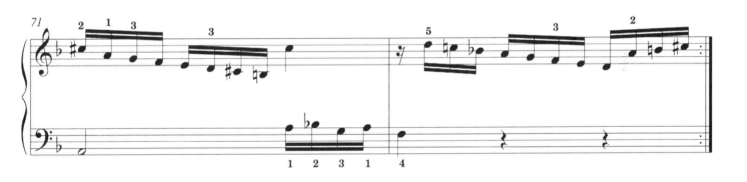

Variation IX

Variation X

Solfeggio in D Major

Johann Christoph Friedrich Bach
(1732– 1795)

Arabesque (Op. 100, No. 2)

Johann Friedrich Burgmüller
(1806– 1874)

Ballade (Op. 100, No. 15)

Johann Friedrich Burgmüller
(1806– 1874)

Tarentelle (Op. 100, No. 20)

Johann Friedrich Burgmüller
(1806– 1874)

81

Fugue in C Major (P. 144, T. 264)

Johann Pachelbel
(1653 – 1706)

March in D Major (BWV Anh. 122)

Notebook for Anna Magdalena Bach

Johann Sebastian Bach
(1658 – 1750)

March in G Major (BWV Anh. 124)

Johann Sebastian Bach
(1658 – 1750)

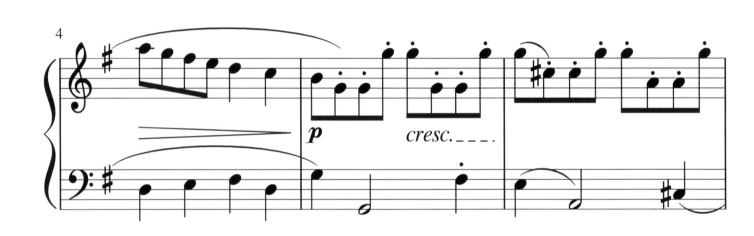

Invention No. 4 in D Minor (BWV 775)

Johann Sebastian Bach
(1658 – 1750)

Invention No. 8 in F Major (BWV 779)

Johann Sebastian Bach
(1658 – 1750)

Invention No. 13 in A Minor (BWV 784)

Johann Sebastian Bach
(1658 – 1750)

Minuet in G Major (BWV 116)

Notebook for Anna Magdalena Bach

Johann Sebastian Bach
(1658 – 1750)

Polonaise in G Minor (BWV Anh. 119)

Notebook for Anna Magdalena Bach

Johann Sebastian Bach
(1658 – 1750)

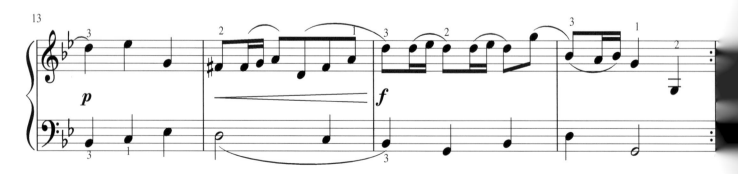

Praeambulum in C Major, BWV 924

Johann Sebastian Bach
(1658 – 1750)

Prélude in C Minor (BWV 999)

Johann Sebastian Bach
(1658 – 1750)

Prélude in C Major (BWV 846)

from "Das Wohltemperierte Klavier" Book I

Johann Sebastian Bach
(1658 – 1750)

Piano

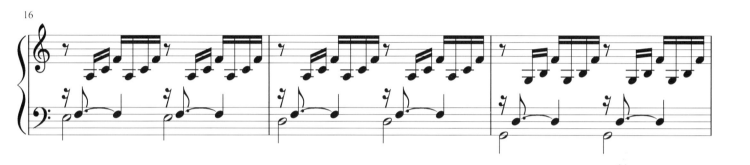

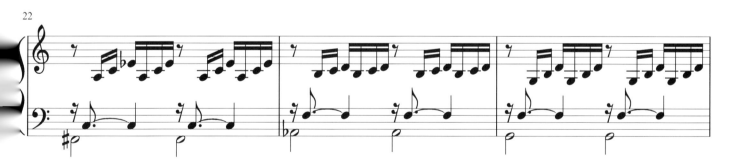

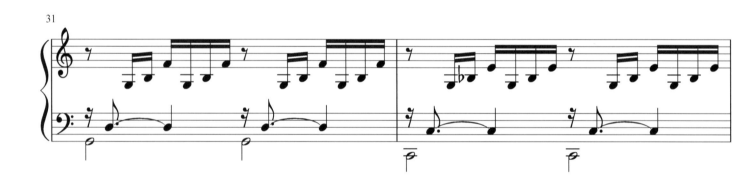

Musette in D BWV Anh 126

from "Anna Magdelena Bach Notebook"

Johann Sebastian Bach
(1658 – 1750)

Für Elise A Minor (WoO. 59)

Ludwig van Beethoven
(1770 – 1827)

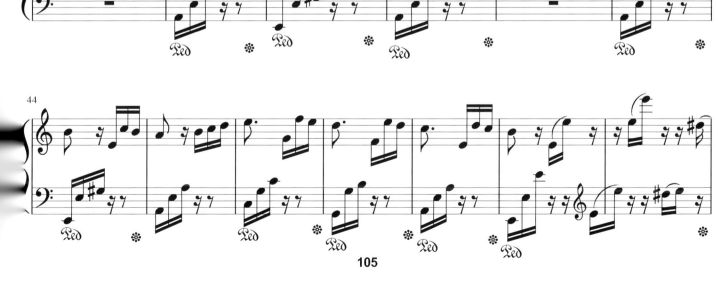

Sonata in G Major (Op. 49, No. 20)

Ludwig van Beethoven
(1770 – 1827)

112

Sonata in G Major (Anh. 5, No. 1)

Ludwig van Beethoven
(1770 – 1827)

Moderato ♩ = 80

Romanze

Sonata in F Major (Anh. 5, No. 2)

Ludwig van Beethoven
(1770 – 1827)

Allegro assai ♩= 100

Rondo

Allegro ♩ = 110

Sonatina I in C Major (Op. 36, No. 1)

Muzio Clementi
(1752 – 1832)

Spiritoso ♩ = 180

The Sick Doll (Op. 39, No. 7)

from "Children's Album"

Pyotr Ilyich Tchaikovsky
(1840 – 1893)

Moderato

129

The Doll's Funeral (Op. 39, No. 8)

from "Children's Album"

Adagio

Pyotr Ilyich Tchaikovsky
(1840 – 1893)

The New Doll (Op. 39, No. 9)

from "Children's Album"

Pyotr Ilyich Tchaikovsky
(1840 – 1893)

Italian Song (Op. 39, No. 15)

from "Children's Album"

Pyotr Ilyich Tchaikovsky
(1840 – 1893)

Moderato assai

sempre staccato il basso

Old French Song (Op. 39, No. 16)

from "Children's Album"

Pyotr Ilyich Tchaikovsky
(1840 – 1893)

Molto moderato

Grand Sonata No. 3 in F Minor (Op. 14, No. 3)

"Concerto without Orchestra"

Robert Alexander Schumann
(1810 – 1856)

135

138

139

142

SCHERZO

146

148

QUASI VARIAZIONI.

Andantino de Clara Wieck. ♩ = 84.

VAR. I.

150

152

153

154

160

Vivacissimo.

Scenes from Childhood - Kinderszenen (Op. 15, No. 7)

"Dreaming - Träumerei"

Robert Alexander Schumann
(1810 – 1856)

Sicilienne (Op. 68, No. 11)

From "Album for the Young"

Robert Alexander Schumann
(1810 – 1856)

First Loss (Op. 68, No. 16)

From "Album for the Young"

Robert Alexander Schumann
(1810 – 1856)

The Wild Horseman (Op. 68, No. 8)

From "Album for the Young"

Robert Alexander Schumann
(1810 – 1856)

Allegro con brio ♩ = 120

Minuet in G Major (K. 1)

Wolfgang Amadeus Mozart
(1756 – 1791)

Minuet in F Major (K. 2)

Wolfgang Amadeus Mozart
(1756 – 1791)

Allegretto grazioso ♩ = 100

Allegro in B-Flat Major (K. 3)

Wolfgang Amadeus Mozart
(1756 – 1791)

Minuet in F Major (K. 5)

Wolfgang Amadeus Mozart
(1756 – 1791)

Minuet in C Major (K. 6)

Wolfgang Amadeus Mozart
(1756 – 1791)

Piano Sonata No.11 in A Major (K.331 / 3)

Wolfgang Amadeus Mozart
(1756 – 1791)

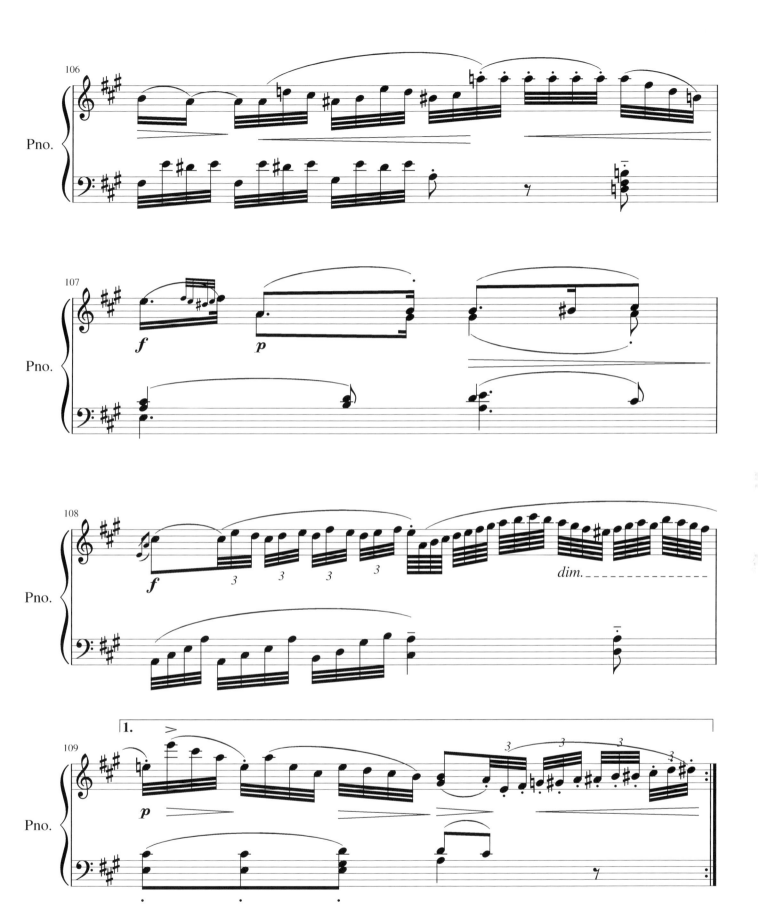

Piano Sonata No. 16 in C Major, 1st Movement, K. 545

Wolfgang Amadeus Mozart
(1756 – 1791)

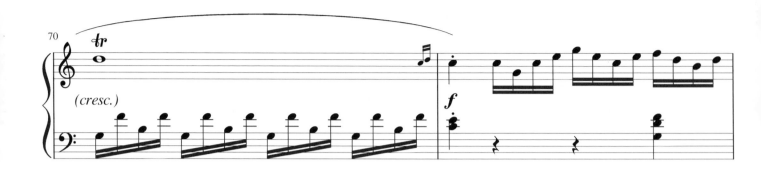

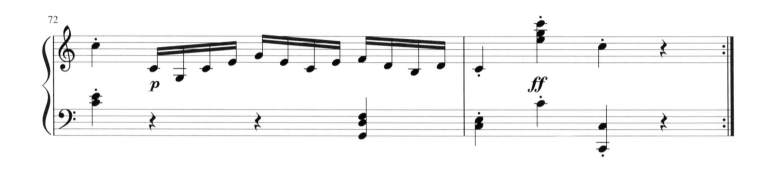

Piano Sonata No. 16 in C Major, 2nd Movement, K. 545

Wolfgang Amadeus Mozart
(1756 – 1791)

Piano Sonata No. 16 in C Major, 3rd Movement, K. 545

Wolfgang Amadeus Mozart
(1756 – 1791)

RONDO
Allegretto

Made in United States
Troutdale, OR
11/27/2023